POETIC VOYAGES OMAGH

Edited by Lucy Jeacock

First published in Great Britain in 2001 by
YOUNG WRITERS
Remus House,
Coltsfoot Drive,
Peterborough, PE2 9JX
Telephone (01733) 890066

HB ISBN 0 75433 212 8
SB ISBN 0 75433 213 6

FOREWORD

Young Writers was established in 1991 with the aim to promote creative writing in children, to make reading and writing poetry fun.

This year once again, proved to be a tremendous success with over 88,000 entries received nationwide.

The Poetic Voyages competition has shown us the high standard of work and effort that children are capable of today. It is a reflection of the teaching skills in schools, the enthusiasm and creativity they have injected into their pupils shines clearly within this anthology.

The task of selecting poems was therefore a difficult one but nevertheless, an enjoyable experience. We hope you are as pleased with the final selection in *Poetic Voyages Omagh* as we are.

CONTENTS

Langfield Primary School

Jemma Bogle	30
Lee McClelland	31
Daryl McCanny	32
Ashley McCauley	33
Stuart McCafferty	34
Matthew Best	35
Leanne Long	36

Loreto Convent Primary School

Caroline McNamee	37
Laura Fitzpatrick	38
Jade McKiernan	39
Orlagh Skelton	40
Cobhlaith Duffy	41
Alice McGlinchey	42
Catherine Madden	43
Caoimhe O'Neill	44
Hannah Torney	45
Kerrie Sharkey	46
Ruth Allen	47
Brogan Chesters	48
Rebecca Gormley	49
Rachel Gormley	50
Shauneen Fox	51
Joanne Lunney	52

Our Lady Of Lourdes Primary School

Ellen Clarke	53
Eva Clarke	54
Mary Fox	55
Dean Fox	56
Shauneen Ferrity	57
Danielle Coyle	58
Alyson Conway	59
Elesha McDermott	60
Peter Teague	61
Kevin McNamee	62

Daniel McElhatton	63
Dermot McCullagh	64
Plunkett McCullagh	65
Catherine McCullagh	66
Mark Carson	67

St Dympna's Primary School

Niall Holland	68
Patrick Irvine	69
Donna McCusker	70
Arlene McCann	71
Rachael Poyntz	72
James McBrearty	73
Laura Slevin	74
Charlene McCarron	75
Ashlene McDonnell	76
Emma McCarron	77
Aaron O'Neill	78
Dean Irvine	79
Sean Teague	80
Kerrie McManus	81
Lauren Birney	82
Edel Goulding	83
Cathy Mullen	84
Louise Slevin	85
Ruairi McNulty	86
Ethan Teague	87
Paula McManus	88
Sean McNabb	89
Ryan McDermott	90

St Macartan's Primary School

Ciaran Slevin	91
Claire McManus	92
Conor McGinn	93

The Poems

NOVEMBER

No cows on the icy hills
No red roses on the smooth grass
No barbecues behind the bushes
No swallows under the wet roofs
No pigs giving birth to babies
No blackbirds chirping in your face
No insects in the muddy ground
November!

Sean Wray (10)
Christ The King Primary School

THE MONSTROUS GREEDY GIANT!

The long-haired giant
With a horrible face
Would chase you into outer space
And . . . if he's not satisfied
He will roar, shout
And knock you out
He splashes through water
With holes in his shoes
What a giant! He's made the news.
He has yellow teeth
And bad BO
Now everybody, let's all go!
Quickly!
Run for your life!

Noel Green (10)
Christ The King Primary School

THE BEACH IN WINTER

Very cold, with mist and fog,
hardly any footprints and very slippery rocks.
Seaweed and seashells scattered all around,
and less rubbish lying on the ground.
Very damp sand, well wrapped up
walking very quickly, a very high tide.
A very sharp wintry wind biting at my cheeks
and very cold sand nipping at my feet.
No picnics, no sunbathing and having no fun.

Natasha Cunningham (11)
Christ The King Primary School

RELAX!

Run a hot bubbly bath
turn on the telly
and have a good laugh
refill my big belly!

Listen to snazzy, jazzy music
sitting in the candlelight
trying with all my might
to stay awake!

Give my dog a makeover
and soon I'm going to have a hangover!
But along with all this
I'm going to
Relax!

Deborah McCollum (11)
Christ The King Primary School

WINTER BEACH

As bare as a newborn chick,
Not a soul sunbathing or having fun,
The tide is coming closer,
Cold water, damp sand,
Everyone wraps up well,
Limpets and oysters hold
On tight to the slippery rocks,
Seaweed and shells washed up
By the high tide.
There is fog and mist
It's hard to see.

Stephanie McGinn (11)
Christ The King Primary School

THE BEACH IN WINTER

When the waves crash against the bay,
The limpets hold tight or else they'll get swept away,
The starfish are waiting for high tide,
To find somewhere else to hide,
When the crabs are crawling,
The night is just about falling,
Then the wind was calling
For the last wave to be falling.

Connor McCann (10)
Christ The King Primary School

COLOURS

Red is a primary colour
bright and shining apple
warm and happy everywhere
a bright hot fire flame
a red rose in the summer garden.

Yellow is the sun shining in the sky
a yellow banana we want to buy
autumn leaves are bright yellow
yellow daffodils blowing in the breeze
barley that ripens in the autumn.

Lisa McFarland (7)
Gortin Controlled Primary School

DIFFERENT COLOURS

Yellow is a warm sun.
A bunch of bananas are bright yellow.
A woolly jumper that you
Wear in winter.

Red is a shiny apple.
A sign that says stop.
A Valentine heart on a
Big red card.

The green leaves are swirling
Around in the wind.
When you are jealous you
Are very green.
The green grass can be wet.

Rachel McKelvey (8)
Gortin Controlled Primary School

WINTER

W inter makes us freezing cold
I cy cold ponds about
N ights are getting long and dark
T rees have lost their leaves
E venings are getting darker
R oaring warm fires to keep us warm.

Sarah-Louise Campbell (8)
Gortin Controlled Primary School

WINTER

W indy cold nights
I cy frost and freezing toes
N ights are getting longer
T rees are looking ghostly in the night.
E arth is frosty in winter
R oaring winds and night.

Kathryn Beattie (8)
Gortin Controlled Primary School

WINTER

W ishing Santa would come soon
I cicles hanging on the roof
N ice presents from Santa
T rees are cold and bare
E very night is windy and cold
R oads are very slippery.

Leticia Blakiston Houston (7)
Gortin Controlled Primary School

WHAT IS GREEN?

Green is a secondary colour,
Sometimes it is dark.
Grass can be green.
Everywhere is bright.
Leaves on the trees are green in spring.
Green can be a green plant.
Hedges can be green.
There's a green colouring crayon,
Very bright.
Green is a signal
Which means go.

Alan Nesbitt (7)
Gortin Controlled Primary School

WHAT IS RED?

Red is shining rubies
In a treasure chest
A primary colour
A sign to say *stop*

When you cut your hand
Red zigzags come out
A big Massey Ferguson coming
Down my road
A little red fox cub
Looking for its mum
A nice sweet apple, juicy and hard

Some juicy strawberries
Nice and soft
A little red robin flying overhead
A red sun setting in the sky
Would you live without red?

Adam McFarland (8)
Gortin Controlled Primary School

THE NEW BULL

My father bought a bull
He got it at the mart
But when he tried to take it home
It wouldn't fit in the cart

My father suggested
We put it in the trailer
And when we got home
We put him in the parlour

When my father
Went to milk the cows
He saw the bull
Drinking tea and having a row

My father got my uncle
To see what was going wrong
Then my uncle said
'That bull has definitely gone ding-dong.'

Adam Fleming (8)
Gortin Controlled Primary School

THE SEA

I can roar
I have fish inside me
My favourite food is ships
I am very salty
I hate the way boats cut me
And I try to drown them
I hate the birds drilling me.

Kyle McIlwaine (8)
Gortin Controlled Primary School

THE MOON

I am the moon
I have eyes as small as stones,
Legs as short as shoes.
I meet fire face to face
And I put it out until it
Turns into ashes.
I have ears as big
As mountains.
At night I can see people
Sleeping in their beds.
They sleep like little
Sleeping bears.

Aaron Campbell (8)
Gortin Controlled Primary School

THE FIRE

I have a face
My face is red
My face is very hot
People feed me wood
I have arms
My arms are very tall
They are very hot as well as my face
You hear me roar loudly
I am very dangerous if you touch me
I am red and orange, sometimes I am yellow
I get big sometimes
When I get very big I burn a house down
I am the dangerous fire.

Lauren McFarland (8)
Gortin Controlled Primary School

FIRE

I have a face
It is very hot
It is burning red and very angry
People give me food
It is wood
Sometimes I die
But I rise again
I stick out my tongue
Because I am hot
I burn people
Because they are as cold as water
Do not touch me
I am scalding
I can burn, it is sore
I have eyes, they are red
Everything I see is red
I can hear all the children shouting
Fire, run for your lives
Because I am fire
I am very dangerous
Do not play with me.

Ashley Whelan (9)
Gortin Controlled Primary School

MY HOMEWORK BOOK

I was doing my homework one night
My book began to smile
It looked at me and said,
'Please throw me for a mile.'

I never went to sleep that night
That book gave me such a fright
I began to scream really loud
And then my book began to bow
'Oh dear,' I whispered to myself.

I took my book to school that day and all the way
He began to say,
'Oh please take me away. I don't like it here'
I gave it to my teacher
Oh how I was dreading that *day!*

The book began to shut its mouth
But I said to my friend
It really did talk.

I got the book back that night
Now the book can't give me a fright.

Lauren Davenport (11)
Gortin Controlled Primary School

THE WIND

I roar and blow like a puffed out person
I screech like an angry person
I can hear the sea banging
Against the rocks
I see the red-hot fire
I hit the moon's shining face
With my cold fast blow
I think I am a bully when I
Speak very loud and friendly
When I speak softly
I am the wind.

Richard McIlwaine (10)
Gortin Controlled Primary School

FIRE

Fire is a roaring man
I travel very far
I break a lot of things
My flames are my skin
The sparks that come out
Of me are my children
I hate water, it makes me go away
My flames are my arms
Lighters are my best friends
Cigarettes are too
Nothing else stands in my
Way but the water.

Kyle Campbell (110
Gortin Controlled Primary School

THE WIND

I push people about
I am strong and
You can not see me
I can destroy the place
If I am mad
I roar and scream and
I get very, very angry.

Stephen Baxter (11)
Gortin Controlled Primary School

FIRE

I rant and rave . . .
Like a cross human.
I raise up too high,
Like a tall human.

I am kept in a cage
Like a mad human.
I am small until I get tall.

I feel happy when I am yellow
I feel angry when I am red.

I speak like a human,
I listen like a human,
I touch like a human,
I throw like a human.

Jason Kennedy (10)
Gortin Controlled Primary School

LAMP POST

I am a lamp post
I stand on this path each day
At night I show the way to home
Where they belong
I am as tall as a tree
I have a head like a giraffe
And the neck of a rocket ship
My baby is as long as a car
I am as fast as a hungry tiger
My eyes glow up in the dark
I show people where to park
That is the life of a
Tall lamp post.

Gareth McKelvey (11)
Gortin Controlled Primary School

THE MOON

I am the moon,
I smile at you.
I am the moon,
I shine at you.
I am the moon,
I have helpers.
I am the moon,
I am shy.
I am the moon,
Sometimes I peep
Out at you.
I am the moon,
I fade away.
I am the moon.

Sarah Fleming (10)
Gortin Controlled Primary School

SEA

I am the sea so blue,
Bluer than blue can be,
I roar with my mouth,
Most of the day though
I soak people when they are in me
All over their body.
My day job is boring
Bored out of my mind I be
I sing to myself
To pass the time for me
The songs that I sing
Are always about me
Look at me, me, me, I am the sea, sea, sea,
I'm as bored as can be, be, be,
Me oh my, me oh my,
I am the blue sea that's me
The sea.

Aaron Houston (11)
Gortin Controlled Primary School

TREE

I am a tree
I can see
the birds are my friends
so watch and see

I can weave
my twigs about
and laugh with glee
I am a tree
watch and see

When I am out
in the cold
I shatter like glass

When I am out
in the sunshine
with my friends
I am all happy again.

Jayne Kennedy (9)
Gortin Controlled Primary School

AUGUSTUS GLOOP

Augustus Gloop, Augustus Gloop
The great big greedy nincompoop,
He eats this, he eats that,
No wonder he's so fat,
Augustus Gloop, Augustus Gloop.

Jonathan Campbell (9)
Gortin Controlled Primary School

THE SUN

I have a face
I have long hair
I have a big smile.

I can see people bathing
I can see an ice cream van
I can melt all the ice cream.

I can hear people squeal
I can make people go brown
When it is night
I go to sleep.

In the morning I wake up
I stare and yawn
I warm up and get myself up in the sky
I look down
A crowd of people are on the beach again!

Gareth Kennedy (9)
Gortin Controlled Primary School

WHAT AM I?

I prowl about in the light,
Or in the dark, dark night.
My claws are sharp,
My teeth are white,
Don't go near me if I'm polite.

I like to eat antelope meat,
And I don't have very big feet.
I have a lovely long tail,
If I was on a boat I'd rip the sail.

Hunters try to kill me,
But they don't have much luck.
They try to get me with a dagger,
Have you guessed it? I'm a tiger.

Jemma Bogle (11)
Langfield Primary School

SPIDERS

Spiders so hairy,
Hairy as wool,
Soft as foam,
Foam so nice,
Nice as hair,
Hair so hairy,
Hairy as spiders.

Lee McClelland (9)
Langfield Primary School

WWF

Albert is a wrestler and he teams up with Test.
Lita's with the Hardyz and she always tries her best.
Ivory is a wrestler who's not so very good
Yet she seems to think that she's a real cool dude.
Essa Rios is a high flyer
And some times he fights like he's on fire.
Never mess with the Undertaker
Or Kane or you will feel a lot of pain!
Stone Cold does the stunner
And after that he is the winner.

Daryl McCanny (10)
Langfield Primary School

DRAGONS

Dragons are huge
With very big teeth
They have scaly skin
And gigantic feet.
Dragons can be any colour
Red and purple or one or the other
Dragons fly with wings of night
People who see them are full of fright.

Fire flaming from their jaws
On their hands they have sharp claws
Their eyes are as red as fire
They fly in the sky higher and higher.
Dragons are very scary
So if you see one be very wary.

Ashley McCauley (9)
Langfield Primary School

DOGS

Dog so big
Dog so small
Dog so soft
Dog so tall.

Dog's teeth so sharp
Dog's tongue so soggy
Dog's tail so long
Dogs don't like moggies.

Stuart McCafferty (10)
Langfield Primary School

SPACE

Space is far away
In the pitch darkness
Where there are lots of planets
As stars in the night sky
With the moon glowing in the dark.

Space is out of this world
Out of every planet
Lots of things are going on out there
The sun is shining very bright
On to the nine planets.

Matthew Best (10)
Langfield Primary School

TIBSEY

Tibsey is a cat,
Cat so soft,
Soft and fluffy,
Fluffy as the clouds,
Clouds in the sky,
Sky so bright,
Bright as the sunlight,
Sunlight shines on Tibsey,
Tibsey lying flat out like a mat.

I see him every day,
Every day at school.
School so boring,
Boring but our cat is adoring,
Adoring and cute,
Cute as a teddy,
Tibsey is cute and cuddly,
Cuddly and sweet,
Sweet as a chocolate cake,
For us to eat.

Leanne Long (9)
Langfield Primary School

AUTUMN

I love the sound of autumn leaves
Going crisp, crisp, crisp
I shake the tree
And they all fall down
But I just gather them up
In a great big mound
I run about and kick them around
Obviously I have to brush them up
But I don't care, I'm just having fun.

Caroline McNamee (8)
Loreto Convent Primary School

THE FALL

Down come leaves,
Floating leaves, dancing leaves,
Swirling leaves, all sorts of leaves,
Come down in autumn.
Dark nights, dark mornings,
Even dark, dark days, lots of dark
Times in autumn.
Heavy rain, light rain, lashing rain,
All sorts of rain in autumn.
Hedgehogs, foxes and even
Squirrels - all sorts of animals
Run around in autumn
Preparing for their long winter sleep.

Laura Fitzpatrick (9)
Loreto Convent Primary School

MUSIC

I love my music so much
I can't, just can't get enough
I turn up my music very loud
And my neighbours have a row

My mum said, 'Turn that down,'
But I say, 'No, I'm listening to it now.'
Then I wake up - I don't turn it up so loud
My neighbours don't make a row

I get CDs nearly every week
And I play them every day
If I didn't have my music
I don't know what I'd do.

Jade McKiernan (9)
Loreto Convent Primary School

FRIENDS

My friend Laura and I,
Go swimming tomorrow,
We have lots of fun,
As we splash in the sun.

Laura's mum leaves me home,
That's when I thought of writing this poem;
So Laura be good,
Laura be kind,
You're one of those friends
That's hard to find.

Orlagh Skelton (9)
Loreto Convent Primary School

THE TREE

I love the colours of
autumn leaves falling to the
ground. I like to see the little
birds hopping from branch to
branch, eating worms they've
found. In spring I watch the
little buds open up to show
the green of tiny
leaves who
look to
the bluest
sky I've
ever seen.
I like to
feel the
roughness
of the bark
under my
hand and think
of the trunk on
which the tree stands.

Cobhlaith Duffy (9)
Loreto Convent Primary School

MY FAVOURITE DAYS

Summer days are bright and warm,
I love playing in the sun.
I get up early in the morning,
And all day have so much fun.
Wintertime, although it's cold,
Is pretty with the snow.
I wrap up in my hat and gloves
And out to play I go.
Christmas Day is wonderful
With lots of gifts and food.
I like to play with my new toys,
Because I've been very good.
Easter comes in springtime
With lots of chocolate eggs.
After eating all of them,
I can hardly move my legs.
But my favourite day comes later,
In October every year,
Because on the twenty-third,
My birthday does appear.
I become a little older
And learn to do much more,
Things like helping with the housework,
Stuff I couldn't do before.
My mum says it was the best,
When I was born that day.
It made her very happy,
To meet me . . . Alice Mae!

Alice McGlinchey (9)
Loreto Convent Primary School

THE VIKINGS

A thousand years ago
The Vikings ruled the world,
But people ask, 'What did Vikings do?'
Vikings came at night
And gave people a fright.
Not the fright you normally have,
They took your children and your wife,
There were only two choices before you die
Or you could run and hide -
But they'd always find you,
Sometimes if you were lucky,
You could work on the boat.

Catherine Madden (9)
Loreto Convent Primary School

HALLOWE'EN SPELL

Now Hallowe'en is near,
It's time for you to hear,
The ingredients of my magic spell
Which I am about to tell.
Rats' tails,
Slime from snails,
Toads' legs,
Some wooden pegs,
Bats' ears,
And puppy dogs' tears
Cows' blood
And dirty mud.
Hubble bubble,
Now there's trouble,
This is my magic mix
Now it's time for some tricks.

Caoimhe O'Neill (8)
Loreto Convent Primary School

THE PIANIST

The pianist sat down to play
Some music about a bay
Quite slow
And very low

What a lovely tune was played
About a girl who stayed
In bed and read, and read, and read.

A lovely concert was played
The girl stayed
In showbiz
But who is this girl we love to see
Well who else could it be
But *me!*

Hannah Torney (8)
Loreto Convent Primary School

AUTUMN

The dancing leaves and twisting leaves
Swaying all day long.
They change colour every autumn
They go from red to golden yellow.
When they're dry they crunch
If they're wet they're soggy,
The night gets darker and
The days get shorter.
The leaves always make a lovely sound.

Kerrie Sharkey (9)
Loreto Convent Primary School

PETS

I love animals, big and small
My hamster Gismo plays on his ball.
All day long he sleeps in his cage
If he got out Mum would be in a rage.

Rosie my dog is black and white
She can jump a very big height
We love to go on a very long walk
It's a terrible pity dogs don't talk.

Ruth Allen (9)
Loreto Convent Primary School

MY DOG MOODY

I have a dog called Moody
He is well trained to fight
And when he growls at night
We have to put him out!

I could say he would not run away
But up in Granny's he would stay
And the next day he would be full of play
My exciting dog called Moody.

When I come home from school
Up he comes and dirties me
And when I say go away
He feels hurt and lonely.

Brogan Chesters (9)
Loreto Convent Primary School

SUMMER

I like summer days best
Because it's sunny and bright
And the children are happy
Because there's no school

I love days by the sea
Splashing about in the waves
Not a care in the world
Oh I do love summer days.

Rebecca Gormley (9)
Loreto Convent Primary School

WINTER

Winter is a lovely time of year.
Best of all Santa comes.
Snow falls gently to the ground.
Children dance and skip around.
They build a snowman
Round and fat
And give him
A great big hat.
Winter days are full of fun.
I love winter best of all!

Rachel Gormley (9)
Loreto Convent Primary School

AUTUMN

Autumn is the time
when the leaves come fluttering down
and float.
In autumn, days get shorter and
autumn nights get longer.
Lots of animals hibernate
because it begins to get cold.
Leaves crackle and crunch at my feet
and when I wake up they're nice and deep.
I go to play in autumn
as I skip and hop along the street.

Shauneen Fox (8)
Loreto Convent Primary School

AUTUMN

Autumn leaves,
Autumn leaves,
Coming from up above trees.

Autumn leaves gold,
Yellow, orange, red and brown come
Twisting and dancing their way down
To the ground until they drown.

As you walk in autumn
You can hear the leaves crunch
Under your feet.

Joanne Lunney (8)
Loreto Convent Primary School

WAITING, WAITING, WAITING

Waiting, waiting, waiting
I'm sick and tired of waiting
Waiting for the bus
I make quite a fuss

Waiting, waiting, waiting
Waiting for my play
I don't like waiting
I wait every day

So I start to complain
I complain to my dad
I complain to my mum
It makes me quite mad

When I am finished
I go up to my bed
No more am I waiting
Just relaxing my head.

Ellen Clarke (9)
Our Lady Of Lourdes Primary School

THE FIRST FROST

On frosty mornings I wake up and see
The frost outside on the trees.
They look frozen like ice
And make me feel cold on my fingers
And toes and all over my clothes.
I go outside and I hear the crunch
Of the grass like it is slippy ice and broken glass.
I go back inside and I take off my
Shoes and my pair of socks that are
Covered with wet and covered with sweat.
I look out the window and I see spider
Webs hanging on the trees and on the branches.
I see my breath in the air like it is
Steam blowing from a kettle.
The sky is so clear that I can see through
Which makes me think that I can see God.
I smell the fresh air outside in the fields
And I smell the flowers blowing in the breeze.
I hear the cars going down the road
And the tractors roaring through the fields.
I hear the dog being called for its food
All covered in mud beside the wood.

Eva Clarke (9)
Our Lady Of Lourdes Primary School

MY PRINCIPAL

Does someone always nag at you?
Well someone does to me.
Like 'Where's your tie?'
I always think to myself I wish I could fly,
Away from school.

He is bad, cross, ugly and very untidy.
He shouts and scolds and I always have
To do what I'm told. It's not fair!
It's not fair! I wish I could get my own
Back on him.

He wears a silly tie, I wish he could forget
It some day just like I do.
He thinks he can sing, but he just goes
Ding! Ding! Ding!

Someday I just wish I could say
Don't be cross, don't be bad, tidy yourself up.
I wish I could scold and scold and
Shout and tell him what to do.

Mary Fox (11)
Our Lady Of Lourdes Primary School

WAITING, WAITING, WAITING

I wait and I wait
for Christmas to come
all the presents I'll get from my mum.
It still has not come, what will I do?
I say to my mum, 'Please tell Christmas to come.'
I wait and wait, Mum still has not told
Maybe, maybe, maybe I was bold.
Finally, finally it has arrived
Christmas, Christmas is now alive.

Dean Fox (9)
Our Lady Of Lourdes Primary School

WAITING, WAITING, WAITING

I'm waiting for Christmas,
With tinsel and snow,
With lights on the tree that twinkle and glow.
Oh but I'm waiting, waiting so!

I'm waiting for Santa with his gifts and toys
To make children happy and bring Christmas joy
Oh but I'm waiting, waiting so!

I'm waiting to hear the birth of the baby,
Born in the stable to Joseph and Mary.
The shepherds and wise men they wait for the light,
For our saviour who'll be born on Christmas night.
Oh but I'm waiting, waiting so!

Shauneen Ferrity (9)
Our Lady Of Lourdes Primary School

WAITING, WAITING, WAITING

I am waiting, waiting, waiting
I am waiting so long
It seems like a year
Since Christmas was gone
I am waiting, waiting, waiting
8760 hours for this very special day.

What is this day, I hear you ask
What else but Christmas day of course.
My stocking is hung, the presents are wrapped
I am waiting, waiting, waiting
For the morning light.
This very day a long time ago
A baby was born.

His birthday we celebrate
The most important thing of all
Now the waiting is over
To another 8760 hours.

Danielle Coyle (9)
Our Lady Of Lourdes Primary School

THE STORY OF THE RAINBOW

One day the colours,
Of the rainbow started to fight.
The yellow said, 'I'm the best,
Because I give out light.'

Then green said, 'No, I am,
Because God chose me,
For the colours of the
Grass, leaves and trees.'

The blue interrupted,
'You only think of land,
What about the sky?
And the sea beside the sand?'

The red, unable to
Stand it any longer
Said, 'I'm the best,
Because I am stronger.'

The purple who was very tall,
Rose to full height,
And said, 'No, I am,
Because I stand for wisdom and might.'

Then rain came,
And said,
'God loves each one of you,
And you've disobeyed.

He loves you all,
The very same,
This is for everyone,
And that's why I came.'

Alyson Conway (10)
Our Lady Of Lourdes Primary School

GROWN-UPS

Did you ever know
your parents are
so hateful
they tell you you can't
go to the disco.

They tell you to go
to bed at nine o'clock
when you want to watch
The Simpsons instead.

They tell you to get
up in the morning
and put your uniform
on and put the kettle on.

It's so embarrassing
when they make fun of you
when you're out with a friend
like talking about me as a baby
how cute I was.

I would love to say
why don't they go to
bed at nine o'clock
and get up in the morning
at seven.

Why don't they put their
uniforms on and put
the kettle on?
I would love to embarrass them!
I think I could!
I think I will!

Elesha McDermott (10)
Our Lady Of Lourdes Primary School

PRESENTS

P   resents and gifts
R   ipped and torn
E   xcited and happy
S   top looking so forlorn
E   vergreen trees
N   ow sparkling with light
T   races of snow
S   howering down at night.

Peter Teague (11)
Our Lady Of Lourdes Primary School

THEM PARENTS

My mum nags
She says bring in them bags
Mop the floor
Close the door

She gives a roar
She hits me, it's sore
She takes my bat
And gives me a slap

Tidy up
Clean that cup
Do your homework
And hurry up

Go to bed
Or you'll be dead
Clean your room
Or this house will be a doom

Clean up your nose
Don't be a doze
Give me help
Or I will give a yelp

And I got mad
Because I was sad
I said, 'Do it yourself
You clean up the shelf.'

Walk the dog
Don't be a hog
You do it
At least a bit.

Kevin McNamee (10)
Our Lady Of Lourdes Primary School

WAITING, WAITING, WAITING

Waiting for my birthday.
I wonder what to get.
A big cake, a small cake,
I haven't decided yet.
I hope they'll just remember
It is in September.
Last year they made me
Have it in December!

Daniel McElhatton (8)
Our Lady Of Lourdes Primary School

WAITING, WAITING, WAITING

I am waiting, waiting, waiting for school to end,
My teacher is just driving me round the bend.
I am doing, doing all my maths,
But I want to go home to have a bath.

There goes the bell, thank God for that,
Oh no! It's the Rouskey bus!
I just can't stand this any more,
I really want to reach for the door.

There goes my bell, hooray! Hooray!
Oh no! I've been daydreaming,
I still have some work to do,
Now I have to stay over to finish it!
Boo!

Dermot McCullagh (9)
Our Lady Of Lourdes Primary School

THE BABYSITTER

From the moment she picks up the phone
To make the call
I can think of nothing
Nothing at all
But her nag
She hops out of her car
Smoking a fag.

As my mum drives
Down the lane
I think what she'll do to me
She'll drive me insane.

Oh no, she approaches
And I'm watching TV
I better turn it off
And jump off the settee.
She's bringing down the phone
Like she usually does
To ring all her friends
And she'll kill us if we make a fuss.

Now I've plucked up my courage
To do what I've wanted to do
Since she came on the bus
That Friday afternoon.

Get off the sofa!
Give me the phone!
When Mum hears of this
You'll be on the first bus home!

Plunkett McCullagh (10)
Our Lady Of Lourdes Primary School

THE FIRST FROST

When I get up I go out to get the bin,
I put on lots of clothes in case I catch a cold.
When I go to lift the milk bottle,
Oh dear! They are too cold, they feel like a frozen ball of ice.
Oh why do I have to do this job?
I go and stamp my feet in the frozen puddles to make them break.
It sounds like the breaking of a glass on a hard floor.
I go back up to the house, my hands are red with cold.
After they warm up, I go out on the sleigh.
I slide and I fall and my legs are all cold.
I look at spider webs, they look like crystal glasses.
When you feel them you can feel the cold going through your hands.
The fences are all frost. It makes me think of Santa and snow.
I am freezing cold and I catch a cold.
My footprints are like big bears and they form a path,
My breath is white like steam out of a kettle.

Catherine McCullagh (9)
Our Lady Of Lourdes Primary School

THE FIREPLACE

My fireplace is brown and it sits on the ground.
It's big and tall but it is not very small,
Smoke and dust comes out at us
Leaving a smell behind it.
We throw in turf and it gives us heat
To keep us snug and warm.
When winter comes we use it a lot
Because it can keep us warm.
We poke it with the poker and the ashes come out
Leaving nothing behind it,
And the fire will go out.
My fireplace is dusty, we clean it all the time,
but it will never shine.

Mark Carson (9)
Our Lady Of Lourdes Primary School

SMELL THE SCENTS, HEAR THE SOUND

Today I think
Only of scents
Not with courage
See vibrant flowers rock with the wind
Fragrances drift by
Deciduous trees stop for shame
Pong from their glory streak
Vivid leaves decay away
Leaving a horrific pong
What about the enchanting scent of the
Autumn night?

Niall Holland (10)
St Dympna's Primary School

JUSTICE

Why is the earth
So joyful with lots of laughter?
But why are there gangs with big bangs
Bullying our estates and breaking hearts?

Why does our heart sink to the
Bottom of the ocean, when it hits the
Bottom it cracks into a million
Pieces which are full of sorrow?

Why do the gangs not feel
Guilty with sorrow?

And why
Can't it stop?

Patrick Irvine (10)
St Dympna's Primary School

INVENTIONS

The light bulb was invented in 1879
It was very handy and had a great shine
Thomas Alva Edison was the inventor
He would have been so rich because of his plan
It was the handiest thing known to man
He put some money into his lining thank God
For the bulb which was so bright and shining.

Donna McCusker (10)
St Dympna's Primary School

AUTUMN WOODS

Today
I think only of scents, musky leaves
coming from the trees begin to fall down.
They stay there and make an odorous smell
and then here comes the breeze.
Leaves begin to blow away so far
the odorous smell goes away too.

Arlene McCann (10)
St Dympna's Primary School

RAINFORESTS

Lions prancing, growling and others with
Wonderful colours like birds and others.
Wonderful and colourful flowers sway to and fro.
Monkeys chattering very loud.
Slithering snakes slither up and down, slimy and scaly.
Wonderful sounds the hummingbird makes and lots more.
Scaly crocodiles going into the water with big sharp teeth.
Parrots like rainbows with colourful tails imitating other birds.
Colourful plants.
Big palm trees with green leaves and a scaly trunk.
Beautiful butterflies flying higher and higher, wonderful colours.

Rachael Poyntz (10)
St Dympna's Primary School

MY SIMILE POEM

I am as good as gold
As steady as a rock
Not as black as coal
As proud as a peacock.

As graceful as a swan
Which is as white as snow
As busy as an ant
Just I know.

I'm as quiet as a mouse
As easy as ABC
As timid as a mouse
And as heavy as as lead.

As swift as a hare
As gentle as a dove
As mad as the March hare
As silent as the grave.

James McBrearty (10)
St Dympna's Primary School

AUTUMN DAYS

Today:
I think only of scents
As I stroll in the wood
Rustling leaves, mildew smell
Beautiful colours, some nice smells
The flowers are purple, violet and blue
The leaves are brown, yellow and curled
The trees stand naked and bare
Gone is the summer
Back is the autumn.

Laura Slevin (11)
St Dympna's Primary School

RAINFOREST

Heavy pattering rain falls down,
Slithery, scaly snakes are around.
Luscious, ruby fruits hanging on trees,
Furry, fat rodents rustling among leaves.

Growling tanned kings of the jungle prancing around,
Chestnut, chattering monkeys swing to the ground.

Psychedelic butterflies fly with the bees,
Brown, hairy coconuts hang on trees.
Squawking, black toucans flying in the rain,
Vivid noisy parrots are really a pain.

Charlene McCarron (11)
St Dympna's Primary School

WHITE WINTER

W hite sheets of snow cover the land
H ard little stones cover the land
I see this landscape through my bedroom window
T iny snowflakes begin to melt away.
E mbrace yourself for a wonderful view.

W onderful views begin to build up.
I saw before me a beautiful panorama.
N obody knows what's going to happen to this beautiful view.
T o keep this beautiful view in front of me, lock it up and throw away the key.
E ventually this picture will fade away but will come back another day
R obin redbreast will have to go and look for food.

Ashlene McDonnell (10)
St Dympna's Primary School

BELFAST GIANTS

Storming down the ice like lightning,
There is no time now to sit in a comfortable chair.
The flashing white you need your sunglasses.
There is no need for them to be on, 'Who Wants To Be A Millionaire?'
It definitely shows they have been eating well,
Puffy grey clouds come out of their mouths.
The winter season can be a lot of fun.
They look cold, as cold as ice.
They need heavy clothing to keep them warm.
You can have such fun at the ice hockey.

Emma McCarron (11)
St Dympna's Primary School

GHOST TRAIN

Getting in the terrifying rollercoaster with a fake ghost.
The chattering sound of rollercoaster moving in house.
The smoke covering us so we can't see much.
The screams and laughter of evil people.
The bats flying over our heads.
The zombies howling for brains.
The ghosts scaring us.
The bad monsters.
The goblins.
Vampires.
Heeeelllllllppp.

Aaron O'Neill (10)
St Dympna's Primary School

TRAINS

I'm a train, a very fast train
I'm a train, a very happy train
I'm a train, a very nice train with carriages
Everyone likes me
I'm a train, a very handsome train with my buffer.

I'm a train, a very fast train
With my carriages I can go
I can go all the way to the station.

I'm a train, a very fast train,
With my metal track,
I can use my buffer
I can pull my carriages.

I'm a train, a very fast train,
With my steam engine driver and
I can carry people
Along tunnels deep under the city.

Dean Irvine (11)
St Dympna's Primary School

WHEN THE WINTER COMES

When the winter comes
snow swoops, animals contract

When the winter comes
ice cracks, cars slip

When the winter comes
children shiver, roads shimmer

When the winter comes
animals hibernate, holiday makers ski

When the winter comes
bugs hide, Jack Frost bites.

Sean Teague (9)
St Dympna's Primary School

IT ISN'T FAIR!

It isn't fair when
we lose the game

It isn't fair when
people call me names

It isn't fair when
my sister dresses the same

It isn't fair when
I was lame

It isn't fair when
I missed the train

It isn't fair when
it started to rain.

'It just isn't fair!'

Kerrie McManus (9)
St Dympna's Primary School

ICE CREAM

Whenever I dream
I dream of ice cream
It goes into my tummy
All creamy and yummy.

Even though it's delicious
It can still be nutritious
It goes into my belly
With strawberry jelly.

It comes in many flavours
You can eat it with wafers
At home or at school
There are no special rules.

Lauren Birney (8)
St Dympna's Primary School

MY CAT

My cat is black and fat,
She lies on her back,
When you poke her,
Her claws are sharp.
In the night she
Scares the mice,
Her eyes are bright
When she stares at
The lights,
When morning comes
My cat is on the mat,
Having a nap,
With a mouse on her lap.

Edel Goulding (10)
St Dympna's Primary School

SLEEPOVER WEEKEND

On Friday when I came home from school
My friends and I played so cool.
In my room my CD went on
We jumped and laughed and sang a song.

As time flew by I couldn't wait
Until tomorrow to celebrate.
I was one year older and felt great,
My friends joined me to sleep until eight.

On Saturday morn we rose, such a clatter
We giggled and laughed and had a great natter.
At four o'clock the party was on,
We played party pieces and I sang a song.

Back to bed with pillows on over our head
I heard the music inside my head.
The jokes began to fly
My friends and I laughed for a while.

Later on on Sunday eve
I said goodbye as they had to leave.
The house was quiet with not a sound
I can't wait till next time to have my friends round.

Cathy Mullen (10)
St Dympna's Primary School

LOVE IS . . .

Mum taking us away for the day,
Getting a lick on the face from a horse,
Playing some games with my friends,
Dad tucking me into bed,
Being cared for in hospital,
Mrs Maguire all the time,
Nana giving me a big hug,
When Laura plays with me,
Mum comforting me,
Wonderful!

Louise Slevin (9)
St Dympna's Primary School

WHEN THE WINTER COMES

When the winter comes,
Snow falls, water freezes.

When the winter comes,
Deers search, icicles dangle.

When the winter comes,
Animals hibernate, doors freeze.

When the winter comes,
Children caper, fires lit.

When the winter comes,
Roads harden, people chill.

Ruairi McNulty (9)
St Dympna's Primary School

THE FRENCH MAN AND WOMAN

There was an old man from France,
Who did the American dance,
He was told to sit down,
So he put on a frown,
And then he got another chance.

A French woman was in a street,
She slipped and fell on some sleet,
Along came some dogs,
Who ripped off her clogs,
So she made a new pair which were neat.

Ethan Teague (9)
St Dympna's Primary School

NOISE, NOISE, AND MORE NOISE

Oh what a place of noise
Of buses, cars and lorries.

Oh what a place of noise
Of music, ice-cream vans and pubs.

Oh what a place of noise
Of dogs, cats and rats.

Oh what a place of noise
Of wind, sleet and snow.

Oh what a place of noise
Of trees and leaves as they blow in the breeze.

Oh what a place of noise in the
Shops of children as they crunch their lollipops.

Can you guess where I am
In the town of course.

Paula McManus (8)
St Dympna's Primary School

THINGS MUMMIES DO

They pick us up if we fall
and if we cry they wipe
away the tears.

They tell us how they love us
and when we are sad they do
things to make us laugh.

When we are down they
come to us and put their
arms around us and tell us silly
things we did when we were babies
and last thing at night they say
is good night, sleep tight.

Sean McNabb (8)
St Dympna's Primary School

LIFE ISN'T FAIR

My daddy's going bald
he has hardly any hair
he often says
'Life isn't fair'

Our TV's stolen
the thieves didn't care
we all know
life isn't fair

The boy down the road
lost his underwear
I heard him cry
'Life isn't fair'

Trees are going bare
it knows
life isn't fair

The man is going out
he had nothing to wear
he said
'Life isn't fair.'

Ryan McDermott (9)
St Dympna's Primary School

GLORY, GLORY, MAN UNITED

Glory, glory, Man United
Scores a goal and we're delighted
With Beckham, Yorke, Giggs and Keane
They make a really brilliant team
Andy Cole shoots and scores
He is the one that fans adore
Scholes is great, Giggs is quick
With a team like this they don't get stick.

Ciaran Slevin (9)
St Macartan's Primary School

MY DOG BRUNO

My dog Bruno is a lovely dog,
But when he goes to play in the grass,
He comes back very smelly.
But no dog or any other pet can replace him
Because I love my dog Bruno.

Claire McManus (9)
St Macartan's Primary School

WRESTLERS!

They are big and hairy,
And very scary.
They bang and bash,
And treat you like trash.
And when they enter the ring,
The bell goes 'Ding-ding'.

They have long hair,
And their clothes would give you a scare.
Chokeslam, Stunner, Pin on the floor,
You can hear the fans shouting for more.
The referee rings the bell, 'Ding-ding',
And hands the belt to the king of the ring.

Conor McGinn (10)
St Macartan's Primary School